W9-AKK-817

BIBLE
TRIVIA CHALLENGE

EVENTS

pil

Publications International, Ltd.

TABLE OF CONTENTS

Genesis..5

Name the Book..19

Which Gospel?...29

Dreams, Visions, and Visitations.............43

Grab Bag...57

Belongings and Gifts...............................71

Food and Feasts......................................81

Parables..91

Music and Verse....................................101

Miracles and Wonders...........................115

TEST YOUR BIBLE TRIVIA KNOWLEDGE!

For many generations, the events of the Bible have given guidance for living, inspiration for faithfulness, and instruction for children. But how well do you really know the nitty-gritty, obscure details? Find out, and see the Bible in a whole new way, with *Bible Trivia Challenge: Events.*

We've split the book into ten chapters, each with fifteen to twenty questions that are perfect for a quick game with your family or the members of your Bible study. The book starts with the stories of Genesis and then takes you through a range of Old Testament and New Testament occurrences. Two chapters, "Which Gospel?" and "Name the Book," will test your knowledge of where certain events are found in the Bible. Other chapters, like "Dreams, Visions, and Visitations" and "Miracles and Wonders," will remind you of God's many interventions in the lives of biblical characters.

Some questions will be easy; others will be challenging. If you get stumped, just turn to the following page. Answers will be found there, along with Biblical references, if you're inspired to reread a favorite story!

It's time to begin. So test your Bible trivia knowledge, learn more about what happened in the Bible, and most of all, have fun!

GENESIS

1. **In the account of creation found in Genesis 1, grass and fruit trees were created on this day.**

   A. The second day
   B. The third day
   C. The fourth day
   D. The fifth day

2. **In the account of creation found in Genesis 1, the stars were created on this day.**

   A. The second day
   B. The third day
   C. The fourth day
   D. The fifth day

1.

B. The third day. See Genesis 1:11–13.

2.

C. The fourth day. See Genesis 1:16–19.

3. **After God told Adam and Eve of the consequences of eating from the fruit of the tree of the knowledge of good and evil, he made them garments from this material.**

A. Fig leaves

B. Skins

C. Olive leaves

D. Leaves from an unspecified plant

4. **How many children did Adam have?**

A. Two

B. Three

C. Four

D. An unknown number

5. **Genesis 5, which lists the descendents of Adam through Noah, says, "And Enoch walked with God: and he was not; for God took him." How old was Enoch when this happened?**

A. 365 years

B. 930 years

C. 969 years

D. The Bible doesn't say.

3.

B. Genesis 2:21 says, "Unto Adam also and to his wife did the Lord God make coats of skins, and clothed them." Previously, Adam and Eve had made themselves clothes from fig leaves. See Genesis 3:7.

4.

D. An unknown number. Cain, Abel, and Seth are the only named children, but Genesis 5:4 says, "And the days of Adam after he had begotten Seth were eight hundred years: and he begat sons and daughters."

5.

A. 365 years. See Genesis 5:21–24.

6. **When does the story of the Tower of Babel take place?**

   A. Before the story of Noah

   B. After the story of Noah but before the story of Abraham

   C. After the story of Abraham but before the story of Joseph

7. **Noah's ark came to rest "upon the mountains of Ararat" during this timeframe.**

   A. After forty days and forty nights

   B. After one hundred and fifty days

   C. In the seventh month, on the seventeenth day of the month

   D. In the tenth month

8. **Genesis 11:31 tells of Abram leaving Ur of the Chaldees. Who traveled with him?**

   A. No one

   B. His nephew Lot

   C. His nephew Lot and his wife Sarai

   D. His nephew Lot, his wife Sarai, and his father Terah

6.

B. After the story of Noah but before the story of Abraham. See Genesis 11.

7.

C. In the seventh month, on the seventeenth day of the month. Per Genesis 8:3, the waters abated after one hundred and fifty days. Per Genesis 8:4, "the ark rested in the seventh month, on the seventeenth day of the month, upon the mountains of Ararat." Per Genesis 8:5, the tops of the mountains were seen in the tenth month.

8.

D. His nephew Lot, his wife Sarai, and his father Terah. See Genesis 11:31.

9. **What event concerning Abraham took place at Beersheba?**

A. Abram's father Terah died.

B. Abram was blessed by Melchizedek, king of Salem.

C. Three visitors of the Lord appeared to Abraham to promise him a son.

D. Abraham made a treaty with Abimelech, king of Gerar.

10. **Abraham saw and offered this animal as a sacrifice when the angel of the Lord told him not to sacrifice his son Isaac.**

A. A kid goat

B. A lamb

C. A ram

D. An ewe

11. **Isaac, like his father Abraham, went to Egypt during a time of famine.**

A. True

B. False

9.

D. Abraham made a treaty with Abimelech, king of Gerar. See Genesis 21:22–32.

10.

C. A ram. See Genesis 22:13.

11.

B. False. In fact, Genesis 26:1–6 notes that during a time of famine, the Lord urged Isaac not to go to Egypt, but to live among the Philistines in Gerar.

12. When Rebekah wanted to fool Isaac into believing Jacob was Esau, a "hairy man," she covered Jacob's smooth hands and neck in this material.

A. Goat skins

B. Cattle skin

C. Snakeskin

D. Lion fur

13. Jacob's wife Rachel took these from her father Laban's home.

A. All the speckled sheep

B. Wages that should have gone to Jacob

C. Laban's household gods

D. Plates of silver

14. When Jacob and his household were leaving Laban and preparing to meet with Esau, on the night before they met Esau, Jacob had a dream of a ladder set between heaven and earth, and angels ascending and descending on it.

A. True

B. False

12.

A. Goat skins. See Genesis 27:15–16: "And Rebekah took goodly raiment of her eldest son Esau, which were with her in the house, and put them upon Jacob her younger son: And she put the skins of the kids of the goats upon his hands, and upon the smooth of his neck."

13.

C. Laban's household gods. Genesis 31 tells the story of how, when Jacob and his wives fled the household of Laban, who felt that Jacob's success had come at his expense, Rachel stole Laban's household gods.

14.

B. False. Jacob dreamed of the ladder earlier in life, when he was fleeing Esau's wrath and going to Laban to find a wife, as his parents had requested. See Genesis 28: 11–18. On the night before he met with Esau, Jacob wrestled with the Lord and won the name Israel. See Genesis 32:24–32.

15. **When Joseph's other brothers wanted to kill him, which brother argued for his life?**

A. Reuben

B. Levi

C. Simeon

D. Judah

16. **How much money did Joseph's brothers gain when they sold him to a merchant caravan?**

A. None

B. Seven pieces of silver

C. Twenty pieces of silver

D. Forty pieces of silver

17. **When Joseph was in prison in Egypt, he interpreted the dreams of a butler and a baker. What did the butler dream of?**

A. Sheaves of wheat

B. Stars, the sun, and the moon

C. A ripe vine laden with grapes

D. Baskets of bread

15.

A. Reuben. See Genesis 37:21–22. Reuben says they should throw Joseph in a cistern rather than kill him. He intends to rescue him and restore him to their father Jacob later. When a caravan passes, however, Judah suggests selling Joseph instead to the merchants instead.

16.

C. Twenty pieces of silver. See Genesis 37:28.

17.

C. A ripe vine laden with grapes. The butler used the grapes to fill Pharaoh's cup. Genesis 40 tells the story.

18. **On being restored to favor, the butler told Pharaoh immediately of the man who had interpreted his dream.**

   A. True
   B. False

19. **When Joseph's brothers came seeking food in Egypt, Joseph demanded that one of them stay in prison in Egypt while the other brothers went and brought Benjamin to Egypt. Which brother stayed?**

   A. Reuben
   B. Levi
   C. Simeon
   D. Judah

20. **When Joseph accuses Benjamin of theft, which brother offers to fulfill Benjamin's punishment in his stead?**

   A. Reuben
   B. Levi
   C. Simeon
   D. Judah

18.

B. False. See Genesis 40:23: "Yet did not the chief butler remember Joseph, but forgat him." It was two years later that the Pharaoh had a dream that required interpretation, and the butler remembered Joseph and brought him to Pharaoh's attention.

19.

C. Simeon. See Genesis 42:24.

20.

D. Judah. See Genesis 44:14–33.

NAME THE BOOK

1. **Which book tells the story of how Miriam was cursed with leprosy for talking against Moses?**

   A. Exodus
   B. Leviticus
   C. Numbers
   D. Deuteronomy

2. **Which book tells the story of how Joshua led the Israelites in battle against the Amalekites while Moses held the staff of God, so that whenever Moses held up his arms, the Israelites were victorious?**

   A. Exodus
   B. Numbers
   C. Deuteronomy
   D. Joshua

3. **The book of 1 Chronicles ends with the coronation of King David.**

   A. True
   B. False

1.

C. Numbers. See Numbers 12.

2.

A. Exodus. See Exodus 17:8–13.

3.

B. False. It ends with his death. See 1 Chronicles 29:26–30.

4. **Which book tells the story of Moses' father-in-law, Jethro, advising him to delegate some of the cases he was being asked to judge to avoid wearing himself out?**

A. Exodus

B. Leviticus

C. Numbers

D. Deuteronomy

5. **Which book contains the story of Balaam's donkey refusing to carry him further, because the angel of the Lord was standing in their way?**

A. Numbers

B. Deuteronomy

C. Joshua

D. Judges

6. **Which book contains the story of the fall of Jericho's walls?**

A. Numbers

B. Deuteronomy

C. Joshua

D. Judges

4.

A. Exodus. See Exodus 18.

5.

A. Numbers. See Numbers 22.

6.

C. Joshua. See Joshua 6.

7. **Which book contains the story of Jael killing Sisera, the commander who was leading an army against Israel?**

A. Numbers

B. Deuteronomy

C. Joshua

D. Judges

8. **Which book contains the story of the Lord turning against Saul for failing to follow the Lord's instructions in the battle against the Amalekites?**

A. Judges

B. 1 Samuel

C. 2 Samuel

D. 1 Kings

9. **Which book tells the story of David's defeat over Goliath?**

A. 1 Samuel

B. 2 Samuel

C. 1 Kings

D. 2 Kings

7.

D. Judges. See Judges 4:17–22.

8.

B. 1 Samuel. See 1 Samuel 15.

9.

B. 1 Samuel. See 1 Samuel 17.

10. Which book tells the story of David dancing before the ark of the Lord as it entered the city of Jerusalem, angering his wife Michal?

A. 1 Samuel

B. 2 Samuel

C. 1 Kings

D. 2 Kings

11. Which book tells the story of Elijah restoring life to the son of a widow?

A. 1 Kings

B. 2 Kings

C. 1 Chronicles

D. 2 Chronicles

12. Which book tells the story of Elijah being taken up to heaven by a whirlwind?

A. 1 Kings

B. 2 Kings

C. 1 Chronicles

D. 2 Chronicles

10.

B. 2 Samuel. See 2 Samuel 6:12–23.

11.

A. 1 Kings. See 1 Kings 17.

12.

B. 2 Kings. See 2 Kings 2.

13. **Which book tells the story of Isaiah healing Hezekiah the king with a poultice of figs?**

   A. 1 Kings

   B. 2 Kings

   C. 1 Chronicles

   D. None of the above

14. **Which book opens with an account of Cyrus, king of Persia, issuing a decree to allow those in exile in Babylon to return to Jerusalem and build a temple?**

   A. Ezra

   B. Nehemiah

   C. Esther

   D. Malachi

15. **Which book contains the story of Ahab and Jezebel conspiring to gain Naboth's vineyard?**

   A. 1 Kings

   B. 2 Kings

   C. Isaiah

   D. Jeremiah

13.

B. See 2 Kings 20:1–7. The story is also told in Isaiah 38.

14.

A. Ezra. See Ezra 1:1–4.

15.

A. 1 Kings. See 1 Kings 21.

WHICH GOSPEL?

1. **Which gospel or gospels contain the account of the wise men bringing gifts of gold, frankincense, and myrrh?**

   A. Matthew only

   B. Mark only

   C. Luke only

   D. John only

   E. Matthew and Luke

2. **Which gospel or gospels contain the story of the wedding at Cana and the miracle Jesus performed there?**

   A. Matthew only

   B. Mark only

   C. Luke only

   D. John only

   E. All of the gospels

3. **The account of Jesus healing the servant of the Centurion is found in all the gospels.**

   A. True

   B. False

1.

A. Matthew only. See Matthew 2. Luke's gospel relates other events surrounding Jesus' birth, but does not speak of the wise men. Neither Mark's gospel nor John's gospel tells details of Jesus' birth.

2.

D. John only. See John 2:1–11. The account does not appear in the other gospels.

3.

B. False. The story is not found at all in the gospel of Mark. As related in Matthew 8:5–13, when Jesus approaches Capernaum, a centurion comes to him to ask for help, but says that Jesus does not have to go to the servant, saying, "I am not worthy that thou shouldest come under my roof: but speak the word only, and my servant shall be healed." A very similar account is found in Luke 7:1–10, although in Luke's account the centurion sends his request for help through intermediaries. John 4:46–54 relays an account of a nobleman at Capernaum who requests help from Jesus for his sick son, whom Jesus heals from afar. Some scholars believe this account in John to refer to the same miracle, while others think it refers to a separate incident.

4. **Which gospel or gospels contain the story of the presentation of Jesus at the temple when he was eight days old, when Joseph and Mary encountered the "just and devout" Simeon and the prophetess Anna?**

A. Matthew only

B. Mark only

C. Luke only

D. John only

E. Matthew and Luke

F. All of the gospels

5. **Which gospel or gospels contain the story of Jesus raising the daughter of Jairus from the dead?**

A. Matthew only

B. Mark only

C. Luke only

D. John only

E. Matthew, Mark, and Luke

F. All of the gospels

4.

C. Luke only. See Luke 2:21–38.

5.

E. Matthew, Mark, and Luke. See Matthew 9:18–26, Mark 5:21–43, and Luke 8:40–56. While all three gospels tell the story of Jesus healing the daughter of a synagogue ruler, only Mark and Luke give the name of the ruler, Jairus.

6. **Which gospel or gospels contain the account of Jesus speaking of "living water" to a Samaritan woman at a well?**

A. Matthew only

B. Mark only

C. Luke only

D. John only

E. Luke and John

F. All of the gospels

7. **Jesus tells the Parable of the Lost Sheep in which gospel(s)?**

A. Matthew only

B. Mark only

C. Luke only

D. Matthew and Luke

E. All of the gospels

8. **The miracle in which Jesus feeds a hungry crowd of 5,000 with five loaves and two fish is found in all the gospels.**

A. True

B. False

6.

D. John only. See John 4:4–26.

7.

D. Matthew and Luke. See Matthew 18:10–18 and Luke 15:4–6.

8.

A. True. See Matthew 14:13–21, Mark 6:31–44, Luke 9:10–17, and John 6:5–15.

9. **Which gospels tell the story of Jesus walking on water after feeding the 5,000?**

A. Matthew and Mark

B. Luke and John

C. Matthew, Mark, and Luke

D. Matthew, Mark, and John

E. All of the gospels

10. **In one gospel account of Jesus walking on water, Peter walks on water to meet Jesus, before his fear makes him doubt and begin to sink. In which gospel does that occur?**

A. Matthew

B. Mark

C. Luke

D. John

11. **The account of Matthias being chosen to replace Judas occurs in which gospel(s)?**

A. Matthew only

B. Mark only

C. Luke only

D. All of the gospels

E. None of the gospels

9.

D. Matthew, Mark, and John. See Matthew 14:22–33, Mark 6:45–52, and John 6:16–21.

10.

A. Matthew. In Matthew's account, Peter walks on the water to go to Jesus, "but when he saw the wind boisterous, he was afraid; and beginning to sink, he cried, saying, Lord, save me." See Matthew 14:30.

11.

E. None of the gospels. It is found in Acts 1:12–26.

12. **All four gospels tell of Jesus carrying the cross. Which gospel or gospels tell of the incident where Simon of Cyrene was pressed into service to help him along the way?**

A. Matthew only

B. Mark only

C. Luke only

D. John only

E. Matthew, Mark, and Luke

F. The story is Christian tradition and not part of the gospels.

13. **The account of the Transfiguration is found in all four gospels.**

A. True

B. False

14. **The account of Jesus appearing after his Resurrection to two men on the road to Emmaus is found only in the gospel of John.**

A. True

B. False

12.

E. Matthew, Mark, and Luke. Simon of Cyrene is mentioned in Matthew 27:32, Mark 15:21, and Luke 23:26. Very little detail is given about the incident in terms of Simon of Cyrene's history or his response to the incident.

13.

B. False. The account of the Transfiguration is found in Matthew 17:1–9, Mark 9:2–8, and Luke 9:28–36, but not the gospel of John.

14.

B. False. The encounter between Jesus and two disciples is told in detail in Luke 24:13–35. The men, one named Cleopas, only recognized Jesus when he broke bread with them. Mark 16:12 says, "After that he appeared in another form unto two of them, as they walked, and went into the country," which some believe might be a reference to the same encounter.

15. Which gospel or gospels tell the story of Jesus washing the feet of the disciples at the Lord's Supper?

A. Matthew only

B. Mark only

C. Luke only

D. John only

E. Matthew, Mark, and Luke

16. We learn the story of "doubting Thomas" in this gospel.

A. Matthew only

B. Mark only

C. Luke only

D. John only

E. The story is Christian tradition and not part of the gospels.

17. The account of Jesus teaching Nicodemus is found in which gospel(s)?

A. Matthew only

B. Mark only

C. Luke only

D. John only

E. Matthew and John

15.

D. John only. While all four gospels tell the story of the Lord's Supper, only John tells of Jesus washing the feet of the disciples as part of it. See John 13:4–12. John's account of the Lord's Supper, in which Jesus talks to his disciples extensively, is significantly longer than that of the other gospels.

16.

D. John only. See John 20:24–29.

17.

D. John only. See John 3:1–21.

18. **All four gospels tell of women going to Jesus' tomb after his death, finding it empty, and telling the disciples. Mary Magdalene is named as one of the women in which gospel(s)?**

   A. Matthew only
   B. Mark only
   C. Luke only
   D. John only
   E. Matthew, Mark, and Luke
   F. All of the gospels

19. **The account of Jesus healing Simon Peter's mother-in-law is found in all the gospels.**

   A. True
   B. False

20. **Which gospel or gospels contain the account of John the Baptist baptizing Jesus?**

   A. Matthew only
   B. Mark only
   C. Luke only
   D. John only
   E. Matthew, Mark, and Luke
   F. All of the gospels

18.

F. All of the gospels. Matthew 28:1 references "Mary Magdalene and the other Mary." Mark 16:1 lists the visitors as "Mary Magdalene, and Mary the mother of James, and Salome." Luke 24:10 speaks of "Mary Magdalene and Joanna, and Mary the mother of James, and other women that were with them." John 20:1 speaks only of Mary Magdalene.

19.

B. False. See Matthew 8:14–15, Mark 1:29–31, and Luke 4:38–39. The incident is not related in the gospel of John.

20.

E. Matthew, Mark, and Luke. See Matthew 3:13–17, Mark 1:9–11, and Luke 3:21–22. Although the gospel of John speaks about John the Baptist's ministry and John the Baptist testifying to Jesus being the Lamb of God, the gospel does not show an actual baptism.

DREAMS, VISIONS, AND VISITATIONS

1. **When the Lord appeared to Abram to make the covenant of circumcision and change his name to Abraham, how old was Abram?**

   A. 90 years old

   B. 99 years old

   C. 100 years old

   D. The Bible doesn't say.

2. **How many angels appeared to lead Lot and his family from Sodom in order to save them from its destruction?**

   A. One

   B. Two

   C. Three

   D. The Bible doesn't say.

1.

B. 99 years old. See Genesis 17:1.

2.

B. Two. See Genesis 19:1.

3. Before Jacob and Esau were born, Rebekah was told, "Two nations are in thy womb, and two manner of people shall be separated from thy bowels." How did she learn this?

A. Her husband Isaac learned it in a dream and told it to her.

B. Her midwife prophesied it.

C. Her mother prophesied it.

D. The Lord told her.

4. In Jacob's dream about a ladder to heaven, the Lord promised that Jacob's descendents would be like this.

A. As countless as the stars

B. As numerous as ants

C. Like the dust of the earth

D. Like a flock of sheep that the Lord would tend

5. In the story of Joseph, when Pharaoh dreamt of seven fat kine (cattle), what happened to them in the dream to indicate that famine would follow a time of plenty?

A. The grain they were eating disappeared, leaving them to starve.

B. They were eaten by seven lions.

C. They were eaten by seven skinny, starving cows.

D. They were chased away by seven skinny, starving cows.

3.

D. The Lord told her. See Genesis 25:21–23.

4.

C. Like the dust of the earth. See Genesis 28:14.

5.

C. They were eaten by seven skinny, starving cows. See Genesis 41:1–4.

6. **Moses was tending his father-in-law Jethro's cattle when he saw the burning bush.**

   A. True
   B. False

7. **When Gideon was called by the Lord to rescue Israel, he received this sign from the Lord.**

   A. His sacrifice of meat and bread was consumed by fire.
   B. A wool fleece left overnight gathered dew even though the ground was dry.
   C. A wool fleece left overnight was left dry even though the ground was wet with dew.
   D. All of the above

8. **Before Samson's birth, this happened to his parents to tell them that their son would deliver the Israelites from the Philistines.**

   A. An angel of the Lord appeared to them.
   B. His mother had a dream.
   C. His father had a dream.
   D. The judge Gideon came to visit them and delivered a prophecy.

6.

B. False. He was tending his father-in-law Jethro's sheep. See Exodus 3:1–3.

7.

D. All of the above. Gideon asked for several signs from the Lord, and they were given to him. See Judges 6:11–40.

8.

A. An angel of the Lord appeared to them. The angel appeared first to Samson's mother, and then to both his parents. See Judges 13.

9. The first time Samuel spoke to the Lord, the Lord told him this.

A. That he would someday appoint a king to Israel.

B. That all of Israel had fallen away from the ways of the Lord.

C. That famine was coming.

D. That Eli's house would be judged for the sins of his sons.

10. In a dream, Solomon asked for wisdom in judging his people, and God was pleased that he asked for wisdom instead of this.

A. Long life

B. Riches

C. The life of his enemies

D. All of the above

11. Three events preceded the Lord appearing to Elijah as "a still small voice." What was the correct order of these events?

A. First a great and strong wind, then an earthquake, and then a fire

B. First an earthquake, then a great and strong wind, then a fire

C. First an earthquake, then a fire, then a great and strong wind

D. First a fire, then an earthquake, then a great and strong wind

9.

D. That Eli's house would be judged for the sins of his sons. See 1 Samuel 3.

10.

D. All of the above. Pleased by Solomon's request, God promised to give him not only "a wise and an understanding heart" but also "riches, and honour: so that there shall not be any among the kings like unto thee all thy days." See 1 Kings 3:5–15.

11.

A. First a great and strong wind, then an earthquake, and then a fire. See 1 Kings 19:11–13.

12. In Isaiah's prophecy about the root of Jesse, it is said that the wolf will dwell with the lamb, and the cow will eat safely near this animal.

A. The leopard

B. The bear

C. The lion

D. A kid goat

13. What happened when Jeremiah was first called by the Lord?

A. He said that he was only a child.

B. He was given a scroll to eat.

C. He left his work as a herdsman and a "gatherer of sycamore fruit."

D. He fled to Tarshish.

14. Daniel dreamed of a great statue made of gold, brass, iron, and clay, which was destroyed by a stone that then became a mountain.

A. True

B. False

12.

B. The bear. See Isaiah 11:6–7: "The wolf also shall dwell with the lamb, and the leopard shall lie down with the kid; and the calf and the young lion and the fatling together; and a little child shall lead them. And the cow and the bear shall feed; their young ones shall lie down together: and the lion shall eat straw like the ox."

13.

A. He said that he was only a child. See Jeremiah 1:4–7. If the other answer choices sound familiar, though, it's because they come from the stories of other prophets. Ezekiel was given a scroll to eat in Ezekiel 2:9—3:4. As told in Amos 7:14–15, before Amos was called to become a prophet, he was a herdsman who tended sycamore trees. It was Jonah who fled to Tarshish. See Jonah 1:3.

14.

B. False. It was King Nebuchadnezzar who had the dream, in which the elements of the statue represented different kingdoms that would eventually be replaced by God's kingdom, although Daniel interpreted it for him. See Daniel 2.

15. **The prophet Zechariah had a vision of this.**

A. A man with a measuring line, used to measure Jerusalem

B. Red, white, and brown horses, which would be sent out throughout the Earth

C. Two olive trees, to symbolize those anointed by the Lord

D. Four chariots, that would go throughout the Earth

E. All of the above

16. **The angel Gabriel appeared to John the Baptist's father Zacharias (Zechariah) when he was doing this.**

A. Sleeping and dreaming

B. Burning incense in the temple

C. Offering a sacrifice of turtledoves

D. The Bible doesn't say.

17. **After the visit from the Magi, Mary, Joseph, and the baby Jesus fled from Herod to Egypt because of this.**

A. The Magi told them to flee Herod.

B. An angel appeared to warn Mary of Herod.

C. Joseph had a dream where an angel warned of danger.

D. None of the above

15.

E. All of the above. See Zechariah 1—6.

16.

B. Burning incense in the temple. See Luke 1:8–12.

17.

C. Joseph had a dream where an angel warned of danger. See Matthew 2:13.

18. **In Acts, the disciple Ananias had a vision telling him to do this.**

   A. To take the desert road, where he met a man from Ethiopia

   B. To find Saul and restore his vision

   C. To host Peter in his house

   D. To go to Macedonia and preach the gospel

19. **While at Cornelius's house, Peter had a vision in which he was told to eat "unclean" foods, leading to his understanding that the gospel message was to be spread to the Gentiles.**

   A. True

   B. False

20. **In Revelation 1:13–16, the author describes one "like the Son of man" who held this in his right hand.**

   A. Seven candlesticks of gold

   B. Seven stars

   C. A sharp two-edged sword

   D. The keys of hell and death

18.

B. To find Saul and restore his vision. Saul, later Paul, had been struck blind on the road to Damascus; Ananias was called to restore his vision. See Acts 9:10–12. All the answer choices do refer to visions described in the book of Acts. Acts 8:26–40 describes how the disciple Philip had a vision that brought him to the road where he met and baptized an Ethiopian eunuch. Cornelius was instructed by an angel in a vision to invite Peter to his house in Acts 10:1–6. Paul had a vision of a man from Macedonia begging him to visit and preach the gospel in Acts 16:9–10.

19.

B. False. Peter was staying at Simon the Tanner's house when he had the vision. Cornelius's men were en route there to invite Peter to stay with Cornelius and teach him. See Acts 10.

20.

B. Seven stars. See Revelation 1:16: "And he had in his right hand seven stars: and out of his mouth went a sharp twoedged sword: and his countenance was as the sun shineth in his strength." Revelation 1:20 says that the seven stars represent the angels of the seven churches whom the author was called to address.

1. **Put these events of Exodus in order.**

   A. Moses left Egypt to avoid punishment for killing an Egyptian who was beating a Hebrew man.

   B. The plague of darkness

   C. The plague of frogs

   D. Moses and Zipporah married.

2. **In Exodus, immediately after the Israelites crossed the Red Sea, they did this.**

   A. They saw a pillar of fire that they followed through the night.

   B. They grumbled against Moses because of a lack of water.

   C. Miriam and Moses led the people in song.

   D. They grumbled against Moses because of a lack of food.

1.

A, D, C, B. Moses left Egypt to avoid punishment and fled to Midian, where he married Zipporah. The plagues occurred after Moses returned to Egypt on God's instructions. The plague of frogs was the second plague, while the plague of darkness was the penultimate plague before the final plague, the death of the firstborn. See Exodus 2:11–22, Exodus 8:1–15, and Exodus 10:21–23.

2.

C. Miriam and Moses led the people in song. See Exodus 15.

3. **The book of Numbers begins with the Lord commanding Moses to do this.**

    A. Go into battle

    B. Take a census

    C. Destroy an idol

    D. Quell a rebellion

4. **In Deuteronomy, the Lord said that men who had done this were exempt from going to war.**

    A. Built a house but not yet dedicated it

    B. Planted a vineyard but not yet eaten of it

    C. Become engaged but not yet married

    D. All of the above

    E. None of the above; all the men were expected to go to war.

5. **In Joshua, which event happened first?**

    A. The Israelites crossing the Jordan River

    B. The fall of Jericho

3.

B. Take a census. See Numbers 1.

4.

D. All of the above. See Deuteronomy 20:5–9. Deuteronomy 24:5 also notes that a recently married man wasn't expected to go to war for one year.

5.

A. The Israelites crossing the Jordan River. See Joshua 3. The fall of Jericho took place shortly thereafter. See Joshua 5:13—6:27.

6. Before Samson told Delilah the truth behind the source of his strength, he told her three false tales. Which of these was **NOT** one of those tales?

A. That he would become weak if tied up with seven thongs that had never been dried

B. That he could be tied up securely with new ropes that had never been used

C. That he would fall deeply asleep if he drank any wine at all

D. That he could be defeated if she wove his hair into a loom

7. When the Israelites wanted a king, Samuel warned them that a king would do this.

A. Make their sons be the king's charioteers

B. Make their daughters be cooks and bakers

C. Give the best of the fields and vineyards to his attendants

D. Take a tenth of the people's flocks

E. All of the above

8. Shortly after Samuel anointed Saul king, Saul began to prophesy.

A. True

B. False

6.

C. That he would fall deeply asleep if he drank any wine at all. See Judges 16:1–22.

7.

E. All of the above. See 1 Samuel 8:10–18.

8.

A. True. After leaving Samuel, Saul met a company of prophets and began to prophesy with them, surprising those around him. See 1 Samuel 10.

9. **Put these events of David's story in order.**

A. David married Abigail.

B. David fled from Absalom.

C. David brought the ark to Jerusalem.

D. David restored the lands of Mephibosheth,
Jonathan's son.

10. **Solomon's brother, Adonijah, tried to claim the kingship in David's old age, but David proclaimed Solomon would rule after him.**

A. True

B. False

11. **After Solomon's death, his sons Rehoboam and Jeroboam fought, and the country divided into Israel and Judah.**

A. True

B. False

9.

A, C, D, B. David married Abigail before he became king. See 1 Samuel 25:39–42. For the story of his bringing the ark to Jerusalem, see 2 Samuel 6. He made peace with Saul's descendent after becoming established as king. See 2 Samuel 9. His son Absalom conspired against him later in his reign. See 2 Samuel 15.

10.

A. True. See 1 Kings 1.

11.

B. False. Jeroboam was not Solomon's son, but an official who had rebelled against Solomon and then returned to foment rebellion against Rehoboam after Solomon's death. The country did divide into two parts, one led by Jeroboam and one led by Rehoboam. See 1 Kings 11:26–40 for Jeroboam's rebellion against Solomon, and 1 Kings 12 for the breaking of the kingdom after Solomon's death.

12. Put these events of King Josiah's story in order.

A. Josiah ordered a renovation of the temple.

B. The prophetess Huldah said that disaster would not come during the time of Josiah because of his repentance and humility.

C. Josiah ordered the altars to false gods torn down.

D. The priest Hilkiah found the Book of the Law, speaking of the punishment God would bring for Israel's disobedience.

13. What did Nehemiah NOT do?

A. Oversee the rebuilding of Jerusalem's walls

B. Act as the Persian king's cup-bearer

C. Act as governor over Judah

D. Rebuild the temple in Jerusalem

14. When Jeremiah was thrown in a cistern, how was he saved?

A. An angel of the Lord drew him out.

B. The Lord sent an earthquake that split open the cistern.

C. A royal official pleaded with the king for his life and was allowed to save him.

D. The king came to visit him and was moved to pity.

12.

A, D, B, C. Josiah ordered the restoration of the temple first. During the restoration, the book of the law was found, foretelling God's wrath since the law had not been followed. Josiah sent men to the prophetess Huldah to receive God's message. Josiah tore down altars afterward. See 2 Kings 22—23.

13.

D. Rebuild the temple in Jerusalem. The other events are told in the book of Nehemiah.

14.

C. A royal official pleaded with the king for his life and was allowed to save him. Ebedmelech, an Ethiopian palace official, interceded with the king on Jeremiah's behalf and was directed to save Jeremiah. See Jeremiah 38.

15. **How many jars of water did Jesus change to wine at the wedding of Cana?**

   A. One

   B. Three

   C. Six

   D. Twelve

16. **When Jesus restored the son of the widow of Nain to life, he did so in response to this.**

   A. She found him and pleaded with him.

   B. Her friends came on her behalf.

   C. He saw the funeral procession and felt compassion for her.

   D. One of the disciples asked if Jesus could help her.

17. **Which of the following events is NOT recounted in Matthew's gospel?**

   A. Jesus telling the parable of the sheep and the goats

   B. Jesus calling Matthew to become a disciple

   C. Jesus preaching the Beatitudes

   D. Jesus being taken up to heaven after his post-Resurrection appearances

15.

C. Six. See John 2:6.

16.

C. He saw the funeral procession and felt compassion for her. See Luke 7:11–17.

17.

D. Jesus being taken up to heaven after his post-Resurrection appearances. Matthew's gospel ends with Jesus commissioning his disciples to go out to teach and baptize. See Matthew 28:16–20. The parable of the sheep and the goats is found in Matthew 25:31–46. The call of Matthew is found in Matthew 9:9. The Beatitudes are found in Matthew 5:2–12.

18. **While Jesus was talking with the Samaritan woman at the well, what were his disciples doing?**

   A. They had gone into town for food.

   B. They were present as well.

   C. They were fishing.

   D. They were arranging a place to stay for the night.

19. **In Colossians, Paul stated that he was writing the letter from prison.**

   A. True

   B. False

20. **In Cyprus, when Paul was teaching an official and a sorcerer and false prophet interfered, Paul said this would be his punishment.**

   A. He would be blinded.

   B. He would become leprous.

   C. He would become mute.

   D. He would die.

18.

A. They had gone into town for food. See John 4:8.

19.

A. True. See Colossians 4:10, which references a fellow prisoner, and his closing note in 4:18.

20.

A. He would be blinded. See Acts 13:6–12.

BELONGINGS AND GIFTS

1. **While in Egypt, Abram acquired the following animals.**

   A. Sheep

   B. Cattle

   C. Camels

   D. Donkeys

   E. All of the above

2. **Isaac gave golden bracelets to Rebekah to indicate that he wanted to marry her.**

   A. True

   B. False

3. **Joseph accused his brothers of stealing this.**

   A. A silver cup

   B. A silver ring

   C. A gemstone bracelet

   D. A gold cup

1.

E. All of the above. See Genesis 12:16.

2.

B. False. Abraham sent a servant to find a bride for his son Isaac, and it was that servant who gave jewelry to Rebekah. See Genesis 24.

3.

A. A silver cup. See Genesis 44:1–2.

4. When the Israelites fled Egypt, they only had the clothes they were wearing and their supplies of unleavened bread.

A. True

B. False

5. The Israelites who spied on the land of Jericho and were hidden by Rahab told her to put this in her window so that her household would be spared in the battle that followed.

A. A cup of silver

B. A red cord

C. A staff

D. A tassel

6. Boaz's kinsman gave up his claim to the land of Naomi's husband Elimelech. What piece of clothing did he take off to renounce the claim?

A. His mantle or cloak

B. A shoe

C. His hat

D. His money pouch

4.

B. False. Along with their flocks and herds, they also brought silver, gold, and clothing given to them by the Egyptians. See Exodus 12:35–39.

5.

B. A red cord. See Joshua 2:17–18.

6.

B. A shoe. It was the custom at the time. See Ruth 4:6–8. Some translations use "sandal" instead of "shoe."

7. How many stones did David have in his shepherd's bag when he faced Goliath?

   A. One
   B. Three
   C. Five
   D. Many

8. The Queen of Sheba brought a large quantity of spices to King Solomon.

   A. True
   B. False

9. Elisha told a widow whose husband's creditors were coming to claim her boys as slaves to ask for these from her neighbors.

   A. Vessels full of oil
   B. Empty vessels
   C. Jugs of wine
   D. Measures of flour

7.

C. Five. See 1 Samuel 17:40.

8.

A. True. 1 Kings 10:10 describes how the Queen of Sheba gifted Solomon with gold, precious stones, and spices. It notes, "there came no more such abundance of spices as these which the queen of Sheba gave to king Solomon."

9.

B. Empty vessels. The widow then poured the "pot of oil" she had into the many vessels, until they all were full, and she could sell the oil to pay her debts and save her sons from servitude. See 2 Kings 4:1–7.

10. In the book of Esther, no one could approach the king if they hadn't been summoned. If they did, they would only be spared death if the king did this.

A. Extended his sandal to be kissed

B. Held out a golden sceptre

C. Extended his signet ring

D. Ordered a cup of wine poured

11. At Bethany, a woman anointed Jesus with costly perfume in a container of this material.

A. Gold

B. Silver

C. Jade

D. Alabaster

12. What kind of perfume did the woman use to anoint Jesus?

A. Myrrh

B. Frankincense

C. Nard

D. Jasmine

10.

B. Hold out a golden sceptre. Xerxes did so to spare Esther's life when she came before him. See Esther 4:11.

11.

D. Alabaster. See Matthew 26:7, Mark 14:3, and Luke 7:37. John's gospel account doesn't specify a material, although unlike the other gospels it does name the woman as Mary, sister of Martha and Lazarus. See John 12:2–8.

12.

C. Nard. See the gospels of Mark and John, where the perfume is identified as "nard" or "spikenard."

13. **In the temple, Jesus praised the widow who put this little amount into the treasury.**

 A. One coin

 B. Two coins

 C. Three coins

 D. A few coins—the Bible doesn't say the exact number

14. **When the soldiers divided up and cast lots for Jesus' clothing, it was seen as a fulfillment of an Old Testament verse from this book and chapter.**

 A. Psalm 22

 B. Psalm 23

 C. Isaiah 9

 D. Isaiah 52

15. **The book of Acts describes how people would bring handkerchiefs or items of clothing that had touched Paul to the sick, who would then be healed.**

 A. True

 B. False

13.

B. Two coins. See Mark 12:42 and Luke 21:2.

14.

A. Psalm 22. See Psalm 22:18. All four gospels talk about the casting of lots for Jesus' clothing, and the gospel of John specifically says that the event is in fulfillment of the scripture. See Matthew 27:35, Mark 15:24, Luke 23:34, and John 19:23–24.

15.

A. True. See Acts 19:11–12.

1. **What did Abraham serve his three visitors who turned out to be sent by the Lord?**

    A. Bread

    B. A calf

    C. Butter and milk

    D. All of the above

2. **When Jacob's sons were preparing to return to Egypt, Jacob told them to bring gifts for Joseph, including these nuts. What were they?**

    A. Peanuts

    B. Cashews

    C. Almonds

    D. Macadamia nuts

3. **In Exodus, manna is described as tasting like this.**

    A. Spices

    B. Wafers made with honey

    C. Bitter herbs

    D. Tasteless

1.

D. All of the above. See Genesis 18:5–8.

2.

C. Almonds. See Genesis 43:11: "And their father Israel said unto them, If it must be so now, do this; take of the best fruits in the land in your vessels, and carry down the man a present, a little balm, and a little honey, spices, and myrrh, nuts, and almonds." Some translations list "pistachio nuts" ahead of almonds.

3.

B. Wafers made with honey. See Exodus 16:31. In Numbers 11:8, however, it's described as tasting like "fresh oil."

4. **In Numbers 6, the Lord decreed that people who took a vow as a Nazirite were prohibited from eating anything that came from this.**

A. The grapevine

B. The olive tree

C. The sea

D. The wheat field

5. **In Numbers 11, while wandering the desert after their exodus from Egypt, the Israelites complained that they missed this food from Egypt.**

A. Fish

B. Cucumbers

C. Melons

D. Leeks

E. All of the above

F. None of the above

6. **1 Samuel 25 tells of a wealthy man named Nabal who provided a feast to David and his men after they had protected his shepherds and sheep.**

A. True

B. False

4.

A. The grapevine. Numbers 6:3–4 says, "He shall separate himself from wine and strong drink, and shall drink no vinegar of wine, or vinegar of strong drink, neither shall he drink any liquor of grapes, nor eat moist grapes, or dried. All the days of his separation shall he eat nothing that is made of the vine tree, from the kernels even to the husk."

5.

E. All of the above. See Numbers 11:5–6: "We remember the fish, which we did eat in Egypt freely; the cucumbers, and the melons, and the leeks, and the onions, and the garlick: But now our soul is dried away: there is nothing at all, beside this manna, before our eyes."

6.

B. False. Nabal refused to help David or his men out, which angered David. Nabal's wife Abigail, when informed that David and his men were marching towards Nabal's lands, set out to prepare a feast for them and beg David's forgiveness.

7. **What meal did Boaz offer Ruth when they first met?**

A. Bread dipped in vinegar

B. Bread dipped in olive oil

C. Honey

D. Corn

8. **What did Jonathan eat that broke the fast that Saul had called for his army when they were fighting the Philistines?**

A. Bread dipped in vinegar

B. Olives

C. Honey

D. Wheat

9. **In 1 Kings 17, Elijah was brought food by this type of bird.**

A. Pigeons

B. Ravens

C. Doves

D. Sparrows

7.

A. Bread dipped in vinegar. Ruth 2 tells of Boaz meeting Ruth, speaking to her of her kindness to Naomi, and offering her bread and vinegar at mealtime.

8.

C. Honey. See 1 Samuel 14:24–45.

9.

B. Ravens. See 1 Kings 17:1–6.

10. **Elisha used flour to purify a pot of stew that was causing the people eating it to feel ill.**

   A. True

   B. False

11. **In exile at the court of Nebuchadnezzar in Babylon, Daniel and his companions proposed to eat and drink these instead of partaking of the royal food and wine.**

   A. Bread and grape juice

   B. Vegetables and water

   C. Honey and water

   D. Bread and wine

12. **John the Baptist was said to eat these.**

   A. Goat's milk and figs

   B. Grains and water

   C. Locusts and wild honey

   D. The Bible does not mention John the Baptist eating.

10.

A. True. 2 Kings 4:38–41 relates how, during a time of famine, Elisha urged his servant to put on a pot of stew for a gathering of men. A servant added a gourd from a "wild vine" to the stew, which caused the men to call the stew "death in the pot." Elisha added flour to the stew and it became edible again.

11.

B. Vegetables and water. See Daniel 1:12. Some translations, including the King James Version, specify "pulse and water" (pulses are legumes) while others more generally say "vegetables and water."

12.

C. Locusts and wild honey. See Matthew 3:4 and Mark 1:6. Some scholars believe that "locusts" refer to the locust tree and its fruit, not the insect.

13. In the Parable of the Prodigal Son, the older brother said bitterly that his father had never given him this.

A. A kid goat so he could feast with his friends

B. A sheep so he could host a celebration

C. A fatted calf at his wedding celebration

D. Pigeons so he could sacrifice to the Lord

14. The gospels of Matthew and Mark tell of Jesus feeding a crowd of 4,000 with the following food.

A. Five loaves and two fish, with twelve baskets left over

B. Seven loaves and a few fish, with seven baskets left over

C. Two loaves and five fish, with five baskets left over

D. Seven loaves and seven fish, with nothing left over

15. In one post-Resurrection appearance, Jesus came to his disciples after they'd had a night of unsuccessful fishing and told them to throw their net to the right side. How many fish did they gather in their nets when they did as he said?

A. 12

B. 40

C. 153

D. 1,000

13.

A. A kid goat so he could feast with his friends. See Luke 15:29.

14.

B. Seven loaves and a few fish, with seven baskets left over. See Matthew 15:32–39 and Mark 8:1–10. This is related as a separate event from the feeding of the 5,000 with five loaves and two fish. For that event, see Matthew 14:13–21, Mark 6:31–44, Luke 9:10–17, and John 6:5–15.

15.

C. 153. See John 21:1–14.

1. **In the Parable of the Rich Fool, what didn't the wealthy fool know?**

   A. That a war was about to come and he would lose his lands.

   B. That he would die that night.

   C. That the crop he had gathered was infested with insects.

   D. That famine would come the following year.

2. **Jesus told the Parable of the Rich Fool in response to this event.**

   A. A wealthy man expressed the desire to follow him.

   B. One of his disciples expressed a desire for wealth.

   C. A man in the crowd wanted Jesus to tell the man's brother to share a family inheritance.

   D. The Bible doesn't say what prompted the parable.

3. **In the Parable of the Prodigal Son, the prodigal son wasted his inheritance over a period of seven years.**

   A. True

   B. False

1.

B. That he would die that night. See Luke 12:13–21.

2.

C. A man in the crowd wanted Jesus to tell the man's brother to share a family inheritance. Jesus responded by telling the crowd a parable that illustrated the dangers of concentrating on earthly wealth instead of their relationship with God.

3.

B. False. The Bible doesn't say how long it took for the prodigal son to squander his inheritance. See Luke 15:11–32.

4. In the Parable of the Good Samaritan, what was the occupation of the Samaritan?

A. Innkeeper

B. Priest

C. Doctor

D. Unknown

5. In the Parable of the Sower, what happened to the seed that fell on rocky ground?

A. Birds ate it.

B. The soil was too shallow for anything to grow.

C. Plants grew but then quickly withered.

D. It brought forth grain, but not enough to feed a family.

6. The Parable of the Mustard Seed describes this happening when the plant reached its full height.

A. It provided shade to farmers.

B. Birds perched in its branches.

C. Its roots broke up rocky ground.

D. All of the above

4.

D. Unknown. The Bible doesn't say the occupation of the Samaritan. See Luke 10:25–37.

5.

C. Plants grew but then quickly withered. See Matthew 13:3–9, Mark 4:3–9, and Luke 8:5–8.

6.

B. Birds perched in its branches. See Matthew 13:31–32, Mark 4:30–32, and Luke 13:18–19.

7. **In Matthew 13:45–46, Jesus compared the kingdom of heaven to this precious object.**

   A. A ruby

   B. A sapphire

   C. A pearl

   D. An emerald

8. **In the Parable of the Lost Sheep, how many sheep did the shepherd have?**

   A. 12

   B. 40

   C. 100

   D. A flock—the number isn't specified

9. **Jesus told the Parable of the Unmerciful Servant, where a servant who had been forgiven debt by his master demanded instant payment from someone who owed a smaller debt to him, in response to this.**

   A. Peter asking how many times he had to forgive someone

   B. Jesus teaching his disciples the Lord's Prayer

   C. A wealthy man asking to become a disciple of Jesus

   D. The scribes and Pharisees bringing him a woman who had been caught in adultery

7.

C. A pearl. See Matthew 13:45–46: "Again, the kingdom of heaven is like unto a merchant man, seeking goodly pearls: Who, when he had found one pearl of great price, went and sold all that he had, and bought it."

8.

C. 100. See Matthew 18:12–13 and Luke 15:4–6.

9.

A. Peter asking how many times he had to forgive someone. See Matthew 18:21–35.

10. **In the Parable of the Lost Coin, what material was the coin that the woman lost and searched for?**

A. Gold

B. Silver

C. Copper

D. Unknown

11. **In the Parable of the Rich Man and Lazarus, the Rich Man talked to this person after death.**

A. Lazarus

B. An angel of the Lord

C. Moses

D. Abraham

12. **In the Parable of the Pharisee and the Tax Collector, the Pharisee bragged about giving this portion of his income to God.**

A. A tenth

B. A quarter

C. Half

D. All of it

10.

B. Silver. See Luke 15:8–10.

11.

D. Abraham. See Luke 16:19-31.

12.

A. A tenth, also known as a tithe. See Luke 18:10–14.

13. **In the Parable of the Ten Virgins, how many were foolish and how many were wise?**

    A. Nine were foolish and one was wise.

    B. Seven were foolish and three were wise.

    C. Five were foolish and five were wise.

    D. All were foolish.

14. **In the Parable of the Two Sons, where one son agreed to work but didn't, and another said he wouldn't but did, what was the work their father asked them to do?**

    A. Working in the vineyard

    B. Harvesting the wheat

    C. Guarding sheep

    D. Unknown

15. **In Matthew's gospel, the king in the Parable of the Great Banquet was throwing a banquet for this occasion.**

    A. His own wedding

    B. His son's wedding

    C. His daughter's wedding

    D. His favored servant's wedding

13.

C. Five were foolish and five were wise. See Matthew 25:1–13.

14.

A. Working in the vineyard. See Matthew 21:28–32.

15.

B. His son's wedding. See Matthew 22:1–14. Luke's gospel also contains a version of the parable, but he tells of a "great man" instead of a king, and the reason for the banquet isn't given. See Luke 14:16–24.

MUSIC AND VERSE

1. **When Miriam led the women in song and dance after the Israelites crossed the Red Sea, she used this instrument.**

   A. A timbrel, or tambourine

   B. A flute

   C. A drum

   D. A lyre, or harp

2. **"For the Lord's portion is his people; Jacob is the lot of his inheritance. He found him in a desert land, and in the waste howling wilderness; he led him about, he instructed him, he kept him as the apple of his eye." Who shared the song containing this verse with Israel, and on what occasion?**

   A. Moses, after the Israelites crossed the Red Sea

   B. Moses, shortly before his death

   C. David, on his coronation

   D. Solomon, on his coronation

1.

A. A timbrel, or tambourine. See Exodus 15:20.

2.

B. Moses, shortly before his death. In Deuteronomy 31, the Lord instructed Moses to write the song and teach it to the children of Israel. For the verses quoted, see Deuteronomy 32:9–10.

3. **When Deborah and Barak sang after the victory over Sisera, the song ended with this line.**

    A. "They ceased in Israel, until that I Deborah arose, that I arose a mother in Israel."

    B. "Awake, awake, Deborah: awake, awake, utter a song: arise, Barak."

    C. "The mother of Sisera looked out at a window, and cried through the lattice, Why is his chariot so long in coming?"

    D. "So let all thine enemies perish, O Lord; but let them that love him be as the sun when he goeth forth in his might."

4. **When Hannah prayed, "My heart rejoiceth in the Lord / mine horn is exalted in the Lord," what was the occasion?**

    A. She had been promised a child by Eli.

    B. She had conceived a son.

    C. She had given birth to Samuel.

    D. She had brought Samuel to the temple to give him to the service of the Lord.

5. **Under David's kingship, 288 men were set aside for "song in the house of the Lord, with cymbals, psalteries, and harps."**

    A. True

    B. False

3.

D. "So let all thine enemies perish, O Lord; but let them that love him be as the sun when he goeth forth in his might." See Judges 5 for the song, and Judges 5:31 for the quoted line.

4.

D. She had brought Samuel to the temple to give him to the service of the Lord. See 1 Samuel 1:21—2:11

5.

A. True. See 1 Chronicles 25:7.

6. **When Saul was tormented by an evil spirit, this would soothe him.**

A. David would play on the flute.

B. David would play on the harp (lyre).

C. His son Jonathan would play on the harp (lyre).

D. His daughter Michal would sing to him.

7. **Saul was jealous about a song that celebrated David's victory in battle. Fill in the blanks in the lyrics: "Saul hath slain his _____, and David his _____."**

A. Tens / Hundreds

B. Hundreds / Thousands

C. Thousands / Ten thousands

D. Enemies / King's enemies

8. **Psalm 3 begins: "Lord, how are they increased that trouble me! Many are they that rise up against me." The psalm was written by David during this time.**

A. When he was fleeing from Saul

B. When he was securing the kingdom from Saul's followers

C. When he was fighting the Ammonites

D. When he was fleeing from Absalom

6.

B. David would play on the harp. See 1 Samuel 16:14–23.

7.

C. Thousands / Ten thousands. See 1 Samuel 18:7.

8.

D. When he was fleeing from Absalom. See the header to the Psalm.

9. **Psalm 51 begins: "Have mercy upon me, O God, according to thy lovingkindness." The psalm was written by David during this time.**

A. When he was fleeing from Saul

B. After Nathan had rebuked him for committing adultery with Bathsheba and arranging Uriah's death

C. When he was fleeing from Absalom

D. Near his death

10. **Solomon learned that his brother Adonijah was claiming the throne because he heard the sound of trumpets and rejoicing from the people.**

A. True

B. False

11. **1 Kings 4, speaking of Solomon's wisdom, says that he created 3,000 proverbs and more than 1,000 songs.**

A. True

B. False

9.

B. After Nathan had rebuked him for committing adultery with Bathsheba and arranging Uriah's death. The psalm continues, "According unto the multitude of thy tender mercies blot out my transgressions. Wash me thoroughly from mine iniquity, and cleanse me from my sin."

10.

B. False. Adonijah set himself up to be king, but Bathsheba and Nathan persuaded David to arrange for Solomon to succeed him. After Solomon was anointed as king, there was a procession with trumpets and pipes. It was Adonijah who heard the sounds of celebration and learned that it was because of Solomon's anointing. See 1 Kings 1.

11.

A. True. See 1 Kings 32–34 for a list of Solomon's accomplishments, which included proverbs, songs, and extensive knowledge of plant and animal life.

12. Ecclesiastes 3:1–8 talks about there being "a time to every purpose under the heaven." Put the verses below in their Biblical order.

A. A time of war, and a time of peace

B. A time to be born, and a time to die

C. A time to weep, and a time to laugh

D. A time to love, and a time to hate

13. The Song of Solomon ends with one of the lovers urging the other to do this.

A. "Make haste, my beloved, and be thou like to a roe or to a young hart upon the mountain of spices."

B. "Let us get up early to the vineyards."

C. "Set me a seal upon thine heart."

D. "Rise up, my love, my fair one, and come away."

14. In Daniel, what was the penalty for not worshipping the golden statue that Nebuchadnezzar had raised whenever "ye hear the sound of the cornet, flute, harp, sackbut, psaltery, dulcimer, and all kinds of musick"?

A. To be thrown in a lion's den

B. To be thrown in a fiery furnace

C. To be imprisoned without bread and water

D. To be cut in pieces and your house made a dunghill

12.

B, C, D, A. The full set of verses reads:

To every thing there is a season, and a time to every purpose under the heaven:

2 A time to be born, and a time to die; a time to plant, and a time to pluck up that which is planted;

3 A time to kill, and a time to heal; a time to break down, and a time to build up;

4 A time to weep, and a time to laugh; a time to mourn, and a time to dance;

5 A time to cast away stones, and a time to gather stones together; a time to embrace, and a time to refrain from embracing;

6 A time to get, and a time to lose; a time to keep, and a time to cast away;

7 A time to rend, and a time to sew; a time to keep silence, and a time to speak;

8 A time to love, and a time to hate; a time of war, and a time of peace.

13.

A. "Make haste, my beloved, and be thou like to a roe or to a young hart upon the mountain of spices." See Song of Solomon 8:14. Option B is from 7:12, option C from 8:6, and option D from 2:10.

14.

B. To be thrown in a fiery furnace. See Daniel 3:4–6. Shadrach, Meshach, and Abednego paid that penalty but went unharmed, astonishing Nebuchadnezzar.

15. When Mary proclaimed, "My soul doth magnify the Lord, and my spirit hath rejoiced in God my savior," she did so at this occasion.

A. When the angel announced that she would be with child

B. When she and Elizabeth met, and the baby leapt in Elizabeth's womb

C. When Jesus was born

D. At the presentation of Jesus at the temple

16. Mary's song concluded with these lines: "to give light to them that sit in darkness and in the shadow of death, to guide our feet into the way of peace."

A. True

B. False

17. Both Mark and Matthew describe Jesus and his disciples singing a hymn on this occasion.

A. On entering Jerusalem for the Passover

B. At the close of the dinner at Simon's house in Bethany

C. At the beginning of the Lord's Supper

D. At the end of the Lord's Supper, before going to the Mount of Olives

15.

B. When she and Elizabeth met, and the baby leapt in Elizabeth's womb. See Luke 1:41–56.

16.

B. False. The lines conclude the prophecy of Zechariah (Zacharias) when his son John the Baptist was born. See Luke 1:67–79.

17.

D. At the end of the Lord's Supper, before going to the Mount of Olives. See Matthew 26:30 and Mark 14:26.

18. **Paul instructed his readers to include music in their worship.**

   A. True
   B. False

19. **James 5:13 says that believers should "sing psalms" on these occasions.**

   A. When they're gathered together
   B. When they're afflicted
   C. When they're merry
   D. When they're sick

20. **In Revelation 5:13, who is described as singing, "Blessing, and honor, and glory, and power, be unto him that sitteth upon the throne, and unto the Lamb"?**

   A. The twenty-four elders gathered around the throne
   B. Ten thousand times ten thousand angels
   C. Every creature which is in heaven, and on the earth, and under the earth, and such as are in the sea
   D. The author of the book

18.

A. True. See Colossians 3:16: " Let the word of Christ dwell in you richly in all wisdom; teaching and admonishing one another in psalms and hymns and spiritual songs, singing with grace in your hearts to the Lord." There's a similar exhortation in Ephesians 5:18–19.

19.

C. When they're merry. The full verse advises: "Is any among you afflicted? let him pray. Is any merry? let him sing psalms."

20.

C. Every creature which is in heaven, and on the earth, and under the earth, and such as are in the sea. Revelation 5 describes a group of twenty-four elders and four creatures who singing a song; they are joined by a multitude of angels, and finally, in the verse in the question, by every creature in heaven and on earth.

Miracles and Wonders

1. **In Exodus, both Moses and the Egyptian magicians turned their rods in snakes, but Moses' rod swallowed up the rods of the Egyptian magicians.**

   A. True
   B. False

2. **In the book of Exodus, which plague came first?**

   A. The plague of blood
   B. The plague of frogs
   C. The plague of gnats
   D. The plague of flies

3. **In the book of Exodus, which event came first?**

   A. God provided water from a rock.
   B. God provided the first instance of manna from heaven.
   C. God gave the Ten Commandments to Moses.
   D. God commanded Moses to have the ark made.

1.

B. False. It was Aaron's staff, not that of Moses, that became a snake. See Exodus 7:8–12.

2.

A. The plague of blood, in which the water sources of Egypt turned to blood, was the first plague. See Exodus 7:14–24.

3.

B. God provided the first instance of manna from heaven. See Exodus 16.

4. **In Joshua 3, when the priests carrying the ark of the covenant led the way across the Jordan River, what sign accompanied them?**

   A. A pillar of fire went before them.

   B. A cloud of smoke went before them.

   C. The river stopped flowing, so the people crossed on dry land.

   D. None of the above

5. **In 1 Samuel 5, when the Philistines captured the art of the covenant and took it to the temple of Dagon, what happened?**

   A. The idol of Dagon fell on its face in front of the ark.

   B. A mysterious fire burned the idol of Dagon.

   C. The priest of Dagon delivered a prophecy of doom for the Philistines.

   D. The temple was flooded.

4.

C. The river stopped flowing, so the people crossed on dry land. See Joshua 3:15–17.

5.

A. The idol of Dagon fell on its face in front of the ark. See 1 Samuel 5. The Philistines kept finding the idol of Dagon face down in front of the ark. A plague of tumors also afflicted the city.

6. 1 Kings 18:38 says, "Then the fire of the Lord fell, and consumed the burnt sacrifice, and the wood, and the stones, and the dust, and licked up the water that was in the trench." This quote belongs to this event.

   A. The Lord responding to a sacrifice of Samuel's

   B. The Lord responding to a sacrifice of David's

   C. The Lord responding to a sacrifice of Solomon's

   D. The Lord responding to a sacrifice of Elijah's

7. Elijah gave instructions for the healing of Naaman, the commander of the army of Syria, from leprosy.

   A. True

   B. False

8. When Elijah was taken up to heaven, he left this behind for Elisha.

   A. A staff

   B. A cloak

   C. His sandals

   D. Nothing

6.

D. The Lord responding to a sacrifice of Elijah's. 1 Kings 18 tells how Elijah confronted the prophets of Baal—Baal did not respond to their sacrifices, but the Lord responded to Elijah's.

7.

B. False. It was Elisha; see 2 Kings 5.

8.

B. A cloak. See 2 Kings 2:13: "He took up also the mantle of Elijah that fell from him, and went back, and stood by the bank of Jordan."

9. When Elisha restored the son of the Shunammite woman to life, what was the first thing the boy did?

A. Gave thanks to the Lord

B. Sneezed

C. Rose from his sickbed

D. Ate some bread dipped in oil

10. God provided this to Jonah while he waited to see what would happen to Ninevah.

A. Food to sustain him

B. A spring of water

C. A vine to shade him

D. A ram to make sacrifice

11. Jesus performed this miracle on the Sabbath, angering the Pharisees.

A. Calming the storm

B. Restoring the daughter of Jairus to life

C. Healing ten lepers

D. Healing a man with a withered hand

9.

B. Sneezed. See 2 Kings 4:35: " Then he [Elisha] returned, and walked in the house to and fro; and went up, and stretched himself upon him: and the child sneezed seven times, and the child opened his eyes."

10.

C. A vine to shade him. See Jonah 4:6.

11.

D. Healing a man with a withered hand. See Matthew 12:10–14, Mark 3:1–6, and Luke 6:6–11.